Introduction

Conservation meets art appreciation for the future of our planet. The true story of the birth of Pongos Helping Pongos: Paintings by Orangutans for Orangutans.

PONGOS
HELPING

PONGOS

What started as simple enrichment for an overactive orangutan living in the big bustling city of Houston, Texas, turned into something much bigger than imagined. Find out how Luna, the orangutan, is helping to save her species, *Pongo pygmaeus,* from the brink of extinction. Living in the zoo, Luna bridges the gap between us and orangutans in the rainforests of Borneo. She proves how much like us they really are and challenges what was once the definition of man... "the tool user".

Your Contribution

50% of the profit from your purchase of this book will go toward the conservation of orangutans in their natural habitat. Thank you, from the bottom of Luna's heart.

For my less hairy little primates,

Shannon, Colin and Clay.

Thank you for sharing the mantle.

Love,

Mom

Special thanks to the Houston Zoo primate staff and volunteers

without whom Luna's legacy would not have been realized.

Pongos Helping Pongos logo and Invitation to Openness image used by permission.

ISBN 978-0-578-94798-3

Printed on paper that comes from sustainably harvested forests.

THE FAIRLY FACTUAL TALE OF
LUNA THE PAINTER

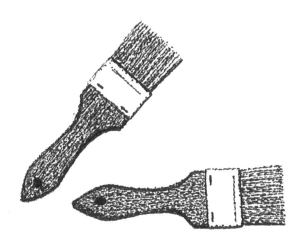

WRITTEN AND ILLUSTRATED BY RHONDA QUISENBERRY

Born on the harvest moon, one cool
September eve, was a little girl named Luna.
She had very kind, caramel-colored eyes and
beautiful, long, rusty-red hair that gleamed like
copper in the sun.

She grew up in the city, in a nice
gated community called...

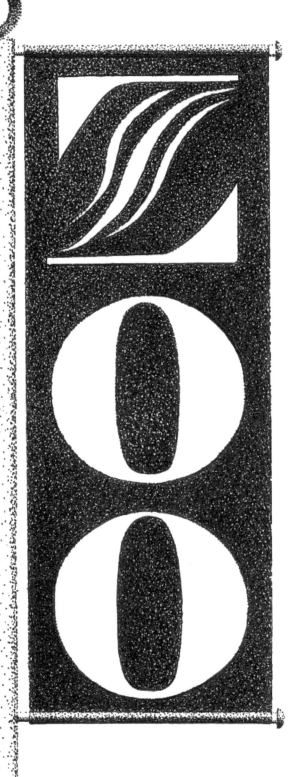

THE ZOO

Human, she was not. But she was like us a lot. Luna was one of the great apes called orangutans.

Chimpanzee

Bonobo

Gorilla

Orangutan

Luna

By age seven, Luna had oodles of energy and loved playing outside. She had a big jungle gym to climb in her yard, and because orangutans are born to live in big jungle trees,

she could climb all the way to the top and hang on with her special orangutan toes.

Sometimes she would take a piece of fabric with her, drape it over her head, then stand up with her arms out and look like ghosty girl!

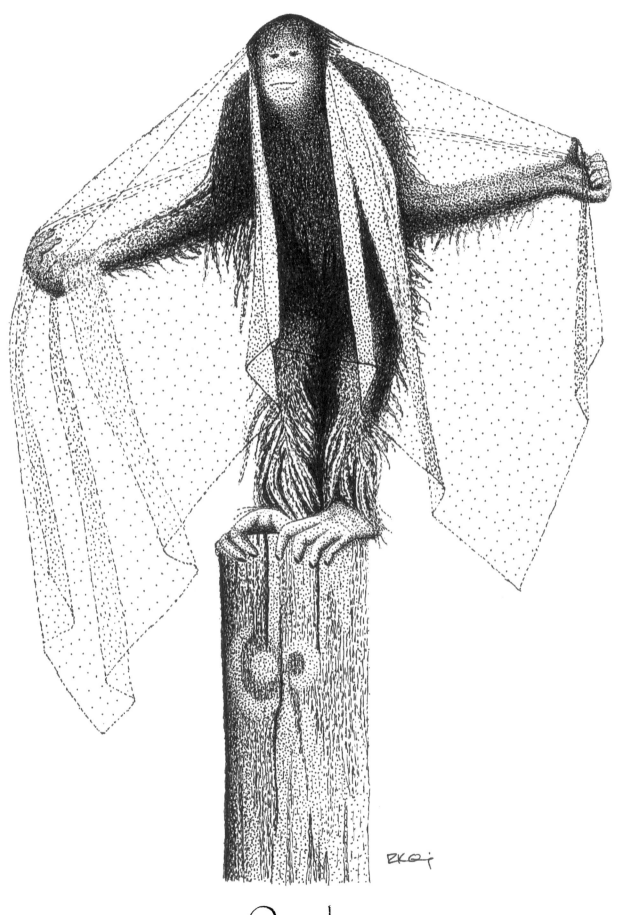

Ooooh

Her mother, Cheyenne, would relax in the grass below while tending to Luna's little brother Elok. He wanted to join his sister in play but could not always keep up with her. In the blink of an eye, she could tumble three times past him, steal his popsicle along the way, and then chase all the sunning turtles back into the stream at the edge of their yard.

Cheyenne and Elok

If Luna got hot she sat under her sprinkler until she was soaking wet. The water dripped down her drenched locks of hair as she covered her head with a box or a big leaf from a banana tree. She would shut her eyes tight, open her mouth and stick out her pink tongue to catch the drops of water, and then quickly cover her face again.

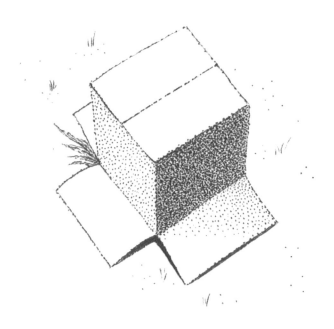

Hot Summer Day

Endless Energy

Some days were just too cold and Luna had to stay inside. Once, while Cheyenne was looking at a magazine (she couldn't read but liked to look at the pictures), Luna tumbled through her hay, grabbed Elok and tumbled backwards with him. Then she stuffed him in a laundry basket!

It was time for Luna to find some new indoor activities.

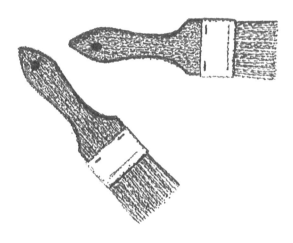

Luna began to paint. First, she tried finger painting on scrap paper, but then she mastered using a brush on canvas. She painted some of her paintings all the same color and others with brilliant mixed colors. Some days she painted with brisk, sweeping strokes, then other days with the finest detail. She could paint while playing under a sheet. She could paint dangling from her feet!

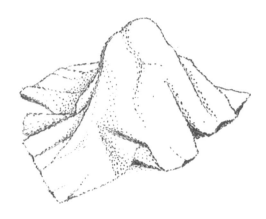

Luna the Painter

Elok tried his hand at it, but he did not do well with a brush, and when he fingerpainted he could not stop licking his fingers! Cheyenne was very good at it, but preferred to spend the quiet time resting.

As Luna produced one masterpiece after another, the other orangutans who lived in the building started to take notice. Even old man Rudi was seen lifting a cheek to sneak a peek.

Rudi

As Luna's paintings sat outside in the sun to dry they began to draw a crowd. All the noise and commotion caused her neighbors, the gibbons, to yell through the bamboo. They always got excited whenever any little thing was going on next door. First Boomer blew up and let out a holler, and then of course Jambi and Susie had to join in. As you might have guessed, this drew an even bigger crowd.

Boomer

When the people who love animals saw the paintings, they wanted to share them with the world. By selling them, they could raise money to help save the rainforest jungles of Borneo, one of two Asian islands on the other side of the world that are the only places left where orangutans live in the wild. They hung the paintings in a famous gallery where other famous artists had hung their paintings and invitations were mailed out for opening night. All the newspapers wrote about it and hundreds of people came to the show.

Borneo Magnified

While Luna was sound asleep in her nest of hay in her room at the zoo, she had no idea what was happening. Ladies in high heeled shoes and men in black ties gathered in front of her paintings to carefully examine each one.

Some liked this one, some liked that one. They compared Luna's artistic style to great modern painters like Jackson Pollock. Three of the paintings won ribbons, one was voted best in show. They all had fancy names like Moonlight in Forest, Borneo Burning and Invitation to Openness.

Invitation to Openness

At the same time, on the other side of the world, another little girl just like Luna was asleep in her nest of leaves high in the trees in the rainforest of Borneo. For the time being, no one was cutting the trees that feed and protect her to make patio furniture. No one was burning the forest down to make way for palm oil plantations. She could still wake up, like Luna, and climb all the way to the tops of the trees to catch raindrops on her tongue. She could rumble through the branches causing the turtles below to dive into the peat swamp and maybe even make her neighbors, the gibbons, holler through the bamboo.

Safe in Mother's Arms

Luna was a hero! Her paintings earned thousands of dollars. She was considered by many to be one of the greatest ape painters of the new age. Without even knowing it, she had turned her endless energy into something that helped save the rainforest and protect her cousins from starving in the wild.

As for herself, living in the zoo, she was no starving artist. There were plenty of juicy popsicles in her future, and for as long as the moon shines on across the darkened sky, so will the tale of Luna the Painter.

Shine on, Luna!

Fun Facts

- The word orangutan (O-rang-oo-tan) means "person of the forest" among the local people on the islands of Borneo and Sumatra.

- Orangutans are the only great apes that live in Asia. The other three, Gorillas, Chimpanzees and Bonobos, live in Africa.

- You can tell the difference between monkeys and apes easily. Monkeys have tails and apes do not. Monkeys, apes and humans are all primates.

- Orangutans have fingers and thumbs like we do, but unlike us, they also have thumbs on their feet! This helps them move easily through the canopy of the rainforest without ever having to go to the ground.

- As male orangutans mature, they develop large throat sacs. They are used to make an eerie series of loud bellows, howls and purrs known as a long call. It announces their position in the forest and can be heard for up to a mile. They also develop large cheek pads that are believed to help project their long call, like cupping your hands around your mouth. Females seem attracted to the males with the largest cheek pads!

- Orangutans can live to be in their fifties. Infants depend on their mothers for up to seven years, longer than any other animal. This means that mother orangutans can only have five babies, or less, in their lifetime.

- Some scientists believe that orangutans are the most intelligent non-human primate, but all great apes think, plan, and problem solve like us. They use, and even make tools. They can count and learn sign language. They are curious. They have emotions and culture, just like we do.

Not So Fun Facts

- There are not enough orangutans left in the world today to fill a football stadium. They are a critically endangered species. Once ranging all through Southeast Asia, they are now confined to two small islands, Borneo and Sumatra, claimed by Malaysia and Indonesia. If changes aren't made they could become extinct very soon. Gone forever!

- Orangutans are arboreal, meaning they live high in the trees and need them to survive. Those same trees create the air you breathe. They are the earths lungs. We also need them to survive.

- Orangutans eat mostly fruit... fruit that grows only in the trees in their rainforest. Unlike some orangutans you might see in zoos, orangutans in their natural habitat rarely go to the ground. They even sleep in nests in the trees, sometimes building two a day by bending and weaving leafy branches into cushy thrones high above any danger from predators, although humans are their biggest threat.

- In recent years orangutans have sadly lost 80% of their rainforest habitat. Illegal logging for exotic lumber, such as teak and mahogany, started the downfall but now an even scarier problem has arisen... palm oil. Huge tracts of primary rainforest on Borneo and Sumatra are being clear cut or burned illegally to make way for palm oil plantations. In the process many orangutans have died and hundreds of baby orangutans have landed in orphanages without their mothers. By the time they are big enough to return to the forest, the forest could be gone!

How You Can Help

- Care.

- Raise awareness by talking to your friends so they will also care.

- Visit your local zoo and participate in any conservation activities to learn more about all the creatures we share our fragile planet with. Educate yourself then share what you have learned on your social media.

- Read labels before making purchases and talk to store managers. Palm oil is in everything from soap to candy. It should be produced in a way that does not harm orangutans or their habitat. The Roundtable on Sustainable Palm Oil® (RSPO®) creates global standards that, when followed, protect eco systems for generations to come. Look for their label on products containing sustainable palm oil. Wood products that carry the Forest Stewardship Council® (FSC®) label also come from responsibly managed forests. Tell your friends to support the caring companies you have discovered. Feel good about your purchases.

- Visit these websites: **redapes.org, orangutan.org, orangutan.com** and **orangutan.or.id** to learn so much more, then give a class presentation at your school. Find a fun way to raise money and donate to them.

- Write letters to Indonesia, Malaysia and US government officials asking them to help stop the illegal activities that are harming and killing orangutans, especially in protected national parks and sanctuaries.

- Remember how much Luna is like you. Imagine what it would be like to be an orangutan in the rainforest. Be a voice for those who cannot speak. Paint a picture for the world to see!

About the Author

Rhonda Quisenberry was a zookeeper of primates at the Houston Zoo for twelve years, the last seven as primary keeper of their seven orangutans. She co-founded "Pongos Helping Pongos: Paintings by Orangutans for Orangutans", an annual art gallery event, organized by the keepers of the Houston Zoo. To date, the paintings have raised over $200,000 in contributions for the conservation of orangutans in their natural habitats on the islands of Borneo and Sumatra. Retired from zookeeping, she now spends her time drawing pointillism images of the special beings once in her charge. With this, her first book, she hopes to raise awareness about the dismal fate of one of the most magnificent creatures on earth, the orangutan.

CPSIA information can be obtained
at www.ICGtesting.com
Printed in the USA
LVHW071259141121
703285LV00002B/50